GRADING EXERCISES IN ENGLISH

BY

A. KITTO-JONES, B.Sc.

ISBN 0 7169 6670 0

ROBERT GIBSON · Publisher
17 Fitzroy Place, Glasgow, G3 7SF

ABOUT THE BOOK

This series of exercises concentrates on the basics of the English language, providing an invaluable bank of multiple choice and other questions for use either in class or at home.

The 15 exercises with over 1400 questions cover some sixty-odd elements of language in such fields as vocabulary, essential grammar, punctuation, spelling, word-building, sentence structure, similes, proverbs and idiomatic expressions.

Teachers can use the tests for periodic assessment of general progress in language work, each test comprising a variety of different language elements.

The tests also serve a diagnostic purpose by showing up weaknesses. The teacher can then put remedial work in hand on such weaknesses (Gibson's *New First Aid in English* is an ideal source book for further study) and apply another of the tests covering the elements in question by way of reassessment.

Pupils transferring from primary to secondary school can profitably check their basic competence in language by working through the book, and those who face a grading or "promotion" test will find this excellent practice for the language elements in such tests.

EXERCISE 1

Write ONE word which can be used instead of the words *in italics*. The first is done for you.

The man gave a present to *the man's* friend. (His).

1. Mary invited Joan to *Mary's* party. (   ).
2. *John and Jim* were home for Christmas. (   )
3. When I had finished the book, I gave *the book* to Joe. (   ).
4. Sam and Peter asked me to lend *Sam and Peter* my camera. (   ).
5. My sister and I gave a party at *my sister's and my* home. (   ).
6. I informed Diana that *Diana* could come. (   ).

———————

One word is missing from each of the following sentences. Write the missing word. One sentence is done for you.

The cat was sitting (on) the mat.

7. The fox jumped (   ) the high wall.
8. The burglar escaped (   ) cover of darkness.
9. The brick fell (   ) the deep water.
10. I put the cloth (   ) the table.
11. I saw him throw the stone (   ) the window.
12. They are building a new bridge (   ) the river.

———————

Punctuate this sentence using these marks: ,   .   ?

13. I have been to London Manchester Singapore and Nairobi
14. I spoke to the doctor at the hospital but he did not tell me much although I was so anxious
15. Which is the quickest way to the station
16. I am fond of fishing but my friend is not so keen so I have to go alone

3

Read this story and then answer the questions that follow:—

One hot summer's day, a crow, that had been flying about for a long time, began to feel thirsty. So she looked around to see if there was any place where she could find some water.

There was no stream near by, and as there had not been any rain for a few weeks, all the little pools were dried up.

At last, she spied a large pitcher at the edge of a corn-field in which some reapers were at work. Full of joy, she flew towards it, hoping to be able to quench her thirst. When she came to the jug and looked in, she saw that it was nearly half-full of water, but the water was quite beyond her reach.

17. What season was it? (Winter; spring; summer; autumn).
18. The crow was feeling (Thirsty; hungry; sleepy; annoyed).
19. The stream was (Far away; on a hill; near by; muddy).
20. Who did the crow see working in the field? (Labourers; roadmen; traders; reapers).
21. The jug was (empty; half-full; full).
22. Which is like a pitcher? (A tuning fork; a spade; a jug; a piano).

Write down a word formed from the word in capitals. All the words will be names (NOUNS) but do not form the word by adding ' er ' or ' ness'. One has been done for you.

SCENE. We admired the beautiful (scenery).

23. APPLAUD; There was loud (   ) at the end of the act.

4

24. ASSIST; She rendered him every (   ).
25. COLLECT; A silver (   ) was taken at the concert.
26. FAMOUS; His (   ) as a soldier is world wide.
27. WISE; He is noted for his (   ).

In each of the following, write a word which RHYMES with the word on the left, and starts with the letter in each bracket. One has been done for you.

HAIR; (Mare) (Care).

28. SIGHT; (R   ) (Wh   ).
29. THREW; (C   ) (Sl   ).
30. NOUGHT; (T   ) (C   ).
31. FEAR; (Ch   ) (P   ).
32. GUILD; (F   ) (B   ).

In the following sentences, add a word which DE-SCRIBES or TELLS MORE ABOUT the word *in italics*. One has been done for you.

The teacher *spoke* (sharply) to the class.

33. The train *sped* (   ) through the station.
34. The crowd *cheered* (   ) as the centre-forward scored.
35. The little girl *wept* (   ) when she heard the news.
36. The old man *walked* (   ) up the steep hill.
37. Everybody *laughed* (   ) at the antics of the clown.

Write ONE word which means the same as or nearly the same as the word in capital letters, and rhymes with

5

the word on the right. The first letter or letters are written for you.

38. FALL (d   ) stop.
39. FEEBLE (w   ) Speak.
40. GLANCE (l   ) Shook.
41. AID (h   ) Yelp.
42. LARGE (g   ) Hate.
43. ENEMY (f   ) Go.

Write the correct form of the VERB written at the beginning. The first one is done for you.

PLAY. He (played) football last Saturday.

44. CATCH. I (   ) a cold at the party.
45. HIDE. He has (   ) the money in the attic.
46. FORGET. I have (   ) to post the letter.
47. GO. He (   ) to Glasgow on the night train.
48. LEAVE. They (   ) the house at noon.

In the bracket is a word SIMILAR in meaning to the one in capitals. Write which one it is. One has been done for you.

ABANDON. The captain refused to (hold; leave; sink; help) the ship.

49. ASTONISHED. I was (excited; pleased; surprised; happy) at the size of the prize.
50. BOTTOM. The workman stood at the (top; rung; foot; middle) of the ladder.
51. CERTAIN. I felt (queer; sure; sorry; satisfied) I could do it.
52. DANGER. The climbers were in great (peril; need; fear; fettle).

6

Read this passage and then answer the questions below:—

Besides the large box in which I was most often carried, the Queen ordered a smaller one to be made for me, because the other was a little too large for my nurse's lap, and took up room in the coach.

This travelling box was square, with a window in the middle of three of the sides, and each window was covered with iron wire on the outside.

On the fourth side, which had no window, two strong hooks were fixed, through which the person who carried me put a belt and tied it about his waist.

53. What carried me? (A tram; a coach; a lorry; a cart).
      Write the one you think is correct.

54. On which side of the box were the hooks fixed? (1st; 2nd; 3rd; 4th).

55. How many windows were in the box?
      (Three; two; four; one).

56. What word is <u>often</u> used instead of MIDDLE?

57. How many windows were covered by iron wire?
      (One; two; three; four).

58. The box was often carried. Which word in the bracket means the same as ' often '?
      (Rarely; frequently; always; never).

59. Give TWO reasons why a smaller box was ordered.

60. To what was the belt tied, after passing it through the hooks?

In each of the following sentences, part of a word is missing. Write the missing letters to complete the word and be careful to spell it correctly. The first is done for you.

There are plenty of (t***t) in the river. <u>(trout).</u>

61. The ship sank to the (b****m) of the river.
62. Mary filled the (g***s) with water.
63. The prisoner made his (e****e) at dusk.
64. The tramp was a (q***r) old man.
65. I am fond of (l**n) meat.
66. I drank some milk to (q****h) my thirst.

In each group there is a word which RHYMES with the word in capitals. Write it down.
67. TIGHT. Weight; late; greet; site; feet.
68. BELIEVE. Leaf; sleeve; strive; sheaf; writhe.
69. WRONG. Rung; string; song; wring; stung.
70. LENGTH. Strength; height; weight; breadth eighth.
71. TOUGH. Bough; cough; rough; dough; below.
72. GREAT. Feat; eat; diet; pleat; fate.

Read the following passage and then choose one of the phrases and write it so that it makes sense:—
Phrases—Think that anyone else / was so beautiful / with plenty of lace / had at least one / good woman / vain and cruel / in her hats / as she was / most beautiful / pure platinum.
73. Now the queen was a .... woman. She wore
74. fine clothes .... on them.
75. She had lovely feathers .... and each of her
76. fingers .... pretty ring on it, one of which
77. was of ....
78. But although she ...., she was certainly not
79. a ....
80. She was proud, ... and she could not
81. bear to .... in the land was so
82. pretty ....

8

Write which is the correct word:—
83. He was the life and (soul, sole) of the party.
84. There is no (plaice; place) like home.
85. We sang a (him; hymn) at the prayer meeting.
86. He cycled round the (coarse; course) before the race.
87. There was a big (hole; whole) in my stocking.
88. I (mist; missed) the train by two minutes.

Here are six sentences that have been divided, and the parts mixed up. Put the correct pairs from Col. A and Col. B together and write the sentence.

COL. A	COL. B
89. A judge	brings our letters
90. A policeman	has a sweet smell
91. The postman	scratches the paper
92. The old lady	wears a helmet
93. This flower	sits in a court
94. My old pen	had a wrinkled face

There are five words in each group. Write them in the correct order with the largest first.
95. Day; week; minute; hour; second . . . .
96. Sheep; mouse; elephant; camel; rabbit . . . . . .
97. Wasp; butterfly; gnat; fly; bird . . . .
98. Millimetre; metre; centimetre; kilometre . . . .
99. Motorway; lane; minor road; path; major road . . . .
100. Bungalow; hut; mansion; palace; cottage . . . .

EXERCISE 2
Write ONE word which can be used instead of the words *in italics*. The first is done for you.
   Jack said that *Jack's* father was employed at the factory. (His).

9

1. Janet's mother asked the teacher if *Janet* could leave early.
2. Jill parked the car but forgot to lock *the car*.
3. The man warned the boys that *the boys* must arrive early.
4. Mother and *mother's* friend are going shopping.
5. Pat and Paul asked me if I would lend *Pat and Paul* my ball.
6. My best friends are May and Susie. *May and Susie* live near me.

Punctuate the following sentences using marks selected from:— . , ? ! "
and write capital letters where necessary.
7. i like apples pears plums and cherries
8. did you ask tom to come to the party
9. i will call again on tuesday said the salesman
10. look out yelled the woodman as the tree started falling

Read the following sentence:—A small shed stood *at* the corner. It can have the same meaning if it is written starting with 'At'.
At the corner stood a small shed.
Now write these sentences, starting with the word *in italics*:—
11. The scout carried a bag *on* his shoulder.
12. I went for a walk *after* I had finished my work.
13. A blackbird was singing *in* the garden.
14. A little brook flowed *through* the garden.
15. The salmon was swimming *in* the pool.
16. There is always snow *on* the top of a high mountain.

10

Here is a selection of phrases that belong to the story below. Choose the most fitting for each part of the story:

to be fed / where the dog / poor tired / near the dog / up jumped / in the fields / into the stall / day's work.

17. Out .... some oxen had been ploughing
18. and when their .... was done, they
19. came back to the shed .... and to rest.
20. One of them went .... and
21. walked up to the manger .... lay.
22. .... the dog at once and began to
23. bark loudly and to snap at the .... ox, and
24. this made him afraid to go ....

Write a word which means the SAME as the word on the left, and RHYMES with the word on the right. The first is done for you.

Great (large) Barge.

25. Pleasant (   ) Twice.
26. Coarse (   ) Muff.
27. Peril (   ) Stranger.
28. Custom (   ) Rabbit.
29. Talk (   ) Squeak.
30. Excuse (   ) Garden.

Write the correct word in each bracket:—

31. To be sorry for means (to rejoice; be glad; repent; delight).
32. The front part of a ship is called the (stern; bow; port; deck).
33. A place where leather is made is a (factory; brewery; works; tannery).
34. A woman in charge of a hospital (Matron; mistress; nurse; governess).

11

35. The men who work on a ship (firemen; crew; members; staff).
36. The end of a railway line (journey; station; terminus; junction).

Read the clues, then write the word in its complete form:—
37. Cannot be beaten .... I-V-NC-B-E.
38. Home for aeroplanes .... - -N-AR.
39. Goods brought into a country .... I-P-RT-.
40. Where beer is made .... -R-W-R-.
41. Fertile spot in a desert .... O-S-S.
42. Opposite to defeat .... -I-TO-Y.

In each of the following groups of words there is ONE that is OPPOSITE in meaning to the one in CAPITALS. Write down which it is:
43. ACCEPT (Retain; regret; accuse; refuse; return).
44. QUESTION (Receipt; answer; write; request; ask).
45. BARREN (Better; faint; ugly; cheap; fertile).
46. HIDE (Reveal; cover; leather; conceal; uphold).
47. FRIEND (Fiend; companion; neighbour; foe; girl).
48. ALWAYS (Seldom; never; sometimes; now; often).

In each of these sentences there are pairs of words that sound the same but are spelt differently. Write down the correct word:—
49. The (flour; flower) grew in the corner of the plot.
50. The (Mayor; mare) gave a banquet last week.
51. I told him not to (medal; meddle) with the car.
52. One of the poles is (hire; higher) than the other.
53. The clerk said he would (write; right) tomorrow.
54. Mary carried the (pale; pail) of milk.

FORM a NOUN from each of these words:—

55. Terrify .... 56. Affectionate................

57. Careful...................... 58. Circular ....

59. Foolish...................... 60. Angry ....

Read this paragraph, then answer the questions that follow:—

The magician did not stay any longer in that street, but hurried away with the magic lamp as fast as he could. He walked until he had got quite outside the city and had reached a lonely spot. It was now quite dark, so he pulled out the magic lamp from the bosom of his robe and rubbed it. The ugly Genie instantly appeared and said, " What do you wish? I am your slave".

61. Which word in the bracket means ' Magician '? (Chemist; conjuror; magistrate; musician.

62. Which of these is similar to a genie? (Ghost; girl's name; fairy; generation).

63. Write what you think is the best reason for rubbing the lamp. (To clean it; to warm it; to make a wish; to polish it).

64. Write the word that means nearly the same as ' instantly '. (Occasionally; immediately; sometimes; slowly).

65. What word could have been used instead of ' slave '?

66. Write a word opposite in meaning to ' ugly'.

67. Write a sentence of your own using the words:— ' Stay any longer'.

68. Where did the magician carry the lamp?

Rearrange each group of words so that they form a sentence. Write it.

69. Tiger; found; is; the; India; in

13

70. Cream; made; butter; is; from
71. Tell; a; me; please; story
72. Television; I; evening; every; watch
73. To; mother; took; the; me; concert
74. Jumped; wall; over; Jack; garden; the

Here are the names of some well-known colours:
Blue; red; green; yellow; brown; black.
Write the correct colour in each of these sentences:
75. Her face was as (   ) as a berry.
76. The (   ) grass made the place look bright.
77. We admired the bunches of (   ) daffodils.
78. After the storm, the sky was (   ).
79. Jitu's muscles were as (   ) as iron.
80. There were lovely (   ) berries on the holly tree.

What is the correct word in each bracket?
81. He (have; has) not been home since Monday.
82. They (begun; began) the work early in the morning.
83. I have (written; wrote) the letter to my uncle.
84. We have (saw; seen) very little of him.
85. They have (taken; took) the parcel to the post-office.
86. I have (showed; shown) him how it is done.

We speak of ONE BOX, but of TWO BOXES. Box is Singular; Boxes is Plural. Write the PLURAL of:—
87. Loaf...................... 88. Army ....
89. Calf .... 90. Church......................
91. Echo...................... 92. Piano ....

Write in the word that is more suitable:—
93. They left the house (until; before) the post arrived.

14

94. I will call (however; whenever) it suits you.
95. (Unless; so) you apologise, I will not come.
96. The taxi waited (until; what) the train arrived.
97. He slipped (Where; as) he climbed the ladder.
98. I cheered (as; because) he passed the post.
99. Nobody passed (however; while) I was waiting.
100. The weather changed (Until; after) I arrived.

EXERCISE 3

One word is missing from each of these sentences.
Write the missing word. The first is done for you.

I met my friend (at) the party.

1. I pushed the note (   ) the door.
2. The picture was hanging (   ) the mantelpiece.
3. I put the sugar (   ) the pantry.
4. On my way home I passed (   ) the station.
5. I called to see him (   ) my arrival.
6. Tube trains travel (   ) the city.

Form a word from the one in capitals, suitable to the rest of the sentence:

7. GLAD. The girl came forward (   ) to meet the Queen.
8. ROGUE. The man was punished for his (   ).
9. CATCH. The wicket-keeper (   ) two men during the match.
10. STEAL. The stray dog has (   ) the meat.
11. DRAW. The sketch was (   ) by a famous artist.
12. FALSE. The clerk tried to (   ) the accounts.

Write a word which RHYMES with the word on the left and begins with the letters in the brackets.

13. WEIGHS. (d   ) (n   ).
14. BRIEF. (ch   ) (l   ).

15

15. SPIRE. (de   ) (sh   ).
16. WIDE. (gl   ) (sl   ).
17. CATCH. (l   ) (sn   ).
18. Glue. (f   ) (ch   ).

In each group of words, write the one that means
the same or nearly the same as the one on the left.
19. DISCOVER. (fail; find; look; lead; ask).
20. FAMOUS. (known; ordinary; eminent; explore;
    popular).
21. SPARKLE. (dull; glitter; glow; smoulder; bright).
22. COMICAL. (curious; stern; usual; famous; funny).
23. FALSE. (true; right; untrue; genuine; teeth).
24. RAISE. (up; lower; top; lift; roof).

After each of these words write a VERB formed from
it:—
25. CREATOR ....   26. MAGNET ....
27. CRITIC ....   28. FOOD....................
29. LIFE ....   30. SIMPLE ....

What is the correct word in each bracket?
31. I think (their; there; they're) going away to-
    morrow.
32. The boy (have; has) finished his work.
33. She hurried (Too; to; two) the station.
34. I was (too; to; two) late to see the wedding.
35. The girls (done; did) some good work for the
    bazaar.
36. He (is; his) not joining the club.

Write ONE word instead of the following:—
37. A place where wild animals live in captivity.
38. A place where films are shown to the public.

16

39. A place where grain is stored.
40. A place where cars are stored.
41. A place where nuns live.
42. A place where soldiers live.

___

Write these words in full. The first is done for you.
ALL'S = ALL is.
43. CAN'T = ...   44. THAT'S = ...
45. WE'LL = ...   46. 'CROSS = ...
47. HASN'T = ...   48. I'VE = ...

___

Write the MASCULINE gender of the word *in italics.*
49. The *actress* (   ) was well received.
50. My *niece* (   ) is staying at our house.
51. The *witch* (   ) was very ugly.
52. The *heroine* (   ) played the part well.
53. The *vixen* was bitten by the hound. (
54. A *tabby-cat* (   ) was caught in the trap.

___

Read this story and then answer the questions that follow:—

The bear was mounting the tree on the other side. He heard her claws scrape and saw her bulge on both sides of the massive tree.

Her eye not being very quick, she reached the fork and passed it, mounting the main stem. Gerard drew breath more freely.

The bear either heard him or found by scent she was wrong. She paused. Presently she caught sight of him. She eyed him steadily, then quietly descended to the fork.

Slowly and cautiously she stretched out a paw and tried the bough. It was a stiff oak branch, sound as iron; instinct taught the creature this. It crawled

17

carefully out on the bough, growling savagely as it came.

From ' THE CLOISTER ON THE HEARTH '
by   Charles Reade

55. Write down the word in the bracket which means the same as MASSIVE. (Large; big; huge; medium).
56. Write down the name of the tree that the bear was mounting. (Elm; oak; holly; ash).
57. Write down the word in the brackets which means the same as CAUTIOUSLY:—(clumsily; carefully; accidentally; recklessly).
58. Which word in the story shows that the bear was a large one?
59. Write down the word in the bracket that means MAIN. (Chief; thick; thin; bough).
60. Write down the word in the bracket that could have been used instead of MOUNTING:—(holding; grasping; climbing; scraping).
61. What word is the opposite to DESCENDED?
62. What enabled the bear to know that the branch was strong enough to hold her weight?

In each of these groups, there is ONE word which is ODD i.e. it is different in some ways from the others. Write it down.
63. Tulip; pansy; carrot; carnation; primrose.
64. Hen; rabbit; goose; turkey; duck.
65. Salmon; cod; eel; whale; trout.
66. Orchid; rose; carrot; carnation; pansy.
67. Germany; Nairobi; Scotland; France; Wales.
68. Ruby; gold; diamond; emerald; sapphire.

18

Write the name of the sound made by each of these:—
69. A MONKEY ....   70. A SWALLOW..............
71. A LAMB ....   72. A BULL ....
73. A SERPENT ....   74. A FROG ....

We speak of a COLLECTION of grapes as a BUNCH of grapes. Write down the name of a collection of:—
75. A .... of pearls.   76. A .... of flowers.
77. A .... of rags.   78. A .... of tools.
79. A .... of diamonds.
80. A .... of drawers.

Write the correct form of the VERB on the left of each sentence:—

Example:—FALL; The little boy has (fallen) down.

81. KNEEL. The bride and bridegroom (   ) at the altar.
82. COME. He asked me if I was (   ) to the match.
83. STEAL. The jewels were (   ) while we were at dinner.
84. HIDE. I found the football (   ) in the cupboard.
85. TEACH. I (   ) in the school for the last seven years.
86. BUILD. The house was (   ) in a short time.

Read the following passage carefully; then answer the questions:—

One bright summer's afternoon, in the year 1575, a tall and fair boy came lingering along Bideford quay, with satchel and slate in hand, watching the shipping and the sailors.

Just after he had passed the bottom of the High Street, he came opposite to one of the many taverns

19

which looked out upon the river. In the open bay window sat merchants and gentlemen, talking over their afternoon glass of wine; and outside the door was gathered a group of sailors, listening earnestly to someone who stood in the midst.

The boy, all alive for any sea-news, took his place among the sailor-lads who were peeping and whispering under the elbows of the men.

From WESTWARD HO!
by Charles Kingsley

87. Which word in the passage tells that the boy was not hurrying?
88. Who were talking to the merchants?
89. Where were the sailors gathered?
90. Write another word meaning TAVERN.
91. Underline the word which tells you what you would expect to see at a QUAY. (Shoppers; A queue; ships; offices).
92. Where were the merchants and gentlemen sitting?
93. What did the boy pass just before he came opposite a tavern?
94. What time in the day did the boy visit the quay? (Morning, afternoon or night?)

———

There are letters missing from one word in each sentence. Write the word.
95. I told the boy to do his work p-o--r-y.
96. The explorer had a good k-o-l-d-e of the district.
97. An e-ep-a-t has a long memory.
98. Mary bought a --z-n eggs.

99. Do you think that --ir-een is unlucky?

100. I have a c--s-n living in Cardiff.

EXERCISE 4

Write down ONE word which can be used instead of the words in *italics*. The first is done for you.

Example:—Dick did not do *Dick's* homework. (His).

1. The girl said that the money was in *the girl's* purse.
2. I fed the dog and then sent *the dog* home.
3. Mother asked Mary if *Mary* would stay to tea.
4. Every morning, Joe starts the car for *Joe's* father.
5. Helen said, " *Helen's* dress is torn."
6. I couldn't enter the park because *the park* was closed.

Read the sentence:—His wife drove *the new car*.

We could write it another way, without changing the meaning:—The *new* car *was driven by* his wife.

Now write these sentences in another way:—

7. Charles Dickens wrote many books.
8. The monitor collected all the books.
9. A strong gale destroyed the building.
10. Stanley Matthews scored the winning goal.
11. The new bowler took the first wicket.
12. The grocer stood in the doorway of his shop.

Read the following phrases, and write them in the sentence to which they belong:—

Under each arm; on her left hand; at every station;
up the path; near the window; under the counter.
13. The chemist was standing ....
14. Mother wheeled the pram ....
15. He carried a parcel ....
16. This train will stop ....
17. He kept the cigarettes ....
18. She wore a ring ....

Write down a word that is OPPOSITE in meaning to the
one on the left, and RHYMES with the one on the right.
The first is done for you:—

Lean (fat) chat.
19. Alive (   ) Bread.
20. Disperse (   ) Father.
21. Love (   ) State.
22. Long (   ) Snort.
23. Difficult (   ) Breezy.
24. Bless (   ) Worse.

Write ONE word which means the same as these:—
25. A man who carries luggage at a railway station is
    a (   ).
26. A man who rides a horse in a race meeting is
    a (   ).
27. A man who carves in stone or marble is a (   ).
28. A man who sells goods by taking bids is an (   ).
29. A man who flies an aeroplane is a (   ).
30. A man who investigates crime is a (   ).

Write down the word in each group which is similar in
meaning to the word in capitals.
31. ABODE. Room; dwelling; path; garden; shed.
32. HEROIC. Dull; haughty; brave; happy; cheerful.

22

33. INTENTION. Purpose; clever; misuse; discover; plot.
34. STICK. Bare; glowed; adhere; solidify; glide.
35. CONCEAL. Reveal; connect; disperse; cover; hide.
36. SORROW. Joy; sympathy; sadness; solitude; envy.

Which is the correct word?
37. Daphne asked her mother for a (piece; peace) of cake.
38. He (mite; might) join the club if you ask him.
39. The squire was shooting (dear; deer) in the park.
40. The teacher (tolled; told) the bell.
41. His (feet; feat) were sore after the long walk.
42. The joiner (bored; board) a small (whole; hole) in the (wood; would).

From the word ABUNDANT, we can form the NOUN 'ABUNDANCE'. Form a NOUN from these words:—
43. MAGICAL (   ).   44. AMUSE (   ).
45. STRONG (   ).   46. SATISFY (   ).
47. THINK (   ).   48. BEGIN (   ).

Read this fable and then answer the questions that follow:—

A hare once met a tortoise and was rude to him. She not only boasted of her own speed in running, but made fun of the slow and clumsy way in which the tortoise moved.

" Slow as I am," said the tortoise, " I am willing to run a race with you whenever you like."

" Very well," replied the hare, " let us start now."

23

So the race began. Away they went, the hare bounding away at great speed, and the tortoise plodding away at a slow and steady pace.

When the hare had reached the middle of the course, she resolved to take a nap, thinking that if the tortoise passed her she could easily overtake him. But she overslept herself, and when she reached the goal, she found that the tortoise had got there before her.

AESOP'S FABLE.

49. Which word here best describes the behaviour of the hare? (Fast; steady; confident; reliable).
50. Which word in the bracket means the same as RESOLVED? (Mean; decided; revived; invited).
51. What is the meaning of " Take a nap? "
52. Which word in the bracket is the OPPOSITE to RUDE? (Pleasant; nasty; impertinent; polite).
53. What word could have been used instead of OVERTAKE?
54. Which group of words shows that the hare was travelling very fast?
55. What do you think is the best reason for the hare losing the race? (She was too slow; she overslept; the tortoise was faster).
56. Which word here means the same as BOASTED? (Bragged; claimed; questioned; knew).

The word DISH means ONE DISH. DISH is SINGULAR NUMBER. The word DISHES is used for MORE THAN ONE dish and is PLURAL NUMBER.
Write the PLURAL NUMBER of:—
57. HOOF............................   58. HERO............................
59. BANJO ....   60. TOOTH ....
61. TROUT ....   62. LADY ....

READ THE FOLLOWING:—

NORTH is to SOUTH as BLACK is to ( )?
The missing word is WHITE because NORTH and SOUTH are OPPOSITE and the opposite of BLACK is WHITE.

Write the missing word:—

63. PEEL is to POTATO as BARK is to ....

64. SEED is to PLANT as EGG is to ....

65. HAND is to FINGER as FOOT is to ....

66. SHIP is to PORT as TRAIN is to ....

67. PACK is to WOLVES as SHOAL is to ....

68. VIXEN is to CUB as GOAT is to ....

———————

We call a collection of cattle a HERD or DROVE of cattle. Write the word for a collection of the following:—

69. Of birds.   70. Of thieves.

71. Of puppies.   72. Of whales.

73. Of bees.   74. Of aeroplanes.

———————

Write each group in order of SIZE or VALUE, beginning with the largest:

75. Monkey; lion; elephant; hare; zebra.

76. Kilogram; tonne; grams; milligrams; decagrams.

77. Day; month; year; week; hour.

78. Centimetre; metre; millimetre; kilometre.

79. Litre; millilitres; decilitre; hectolitre.
80. Gnat; wasp; butterfly; bird; fly.

Read this passage and then answer the questions below:

In the United States, nearly a hundred years ago, oxen were used to pull the heavy wagons in the wagon trains because they could withstand the hardships of the plains better than the horses did. They could go longer without water, and needed less food, for they could live on the scant prairie grasses much better than horses or mules could. Ox trains usually travelled ten to twelve miles a day when loaded, but when returning with empty wagons, they made as many as twenty miles a day.

At night the oxen were allowed to graze after they had been unyoked, but they were always guarded, the men taking turns at the task. Often oxen were made sick when they were bitten on the noses or feet by rattlesnakes that struck at them as they grazed.

From 'Buffalo Bill'.
—Ralph Johnston

81. Give ONE reason why Oxen were preferred to mules or horses.
82. About how far could a team of oxen draw a wagon loaded—in one day?
83. What word could you use instead of UNYOKED?
84. On what did the oxen feed?
85. What made the oxen sick?
86. What word could have been used instead of GUARDED?
87. At what time did the oxen graze?
88. Who guarded them while they were grazing?

In each sentence write one of these:—

In which; of which; to which.

89. I have a locker .... I keep my books.
90. I showed him the place .... I was going.
91. This is the flower .... the teacher was speaking.
92. I have a small box .... I keep my toys.
93. The book .... you told me is in the cupboard.
94. .... town is the bus going?

An ENGLISH town is the description of a town in ENGLAND.

ENGLISH is an ADJECTIVE formed from ENGLAND.

Write down the ADJECTIVE formed from the word in capital letters:

95. Bacon from DENMARK is called (   ) bacon.
96. Lamb from WALES is called (   ) lamb.
97. Watches from SWITZERLAND are called (   ) watches.
98. Coffee from Kenya is called (   ) coffee.
99. Cheese from HOLLAND is called (   ) cheese.
100 Rice from CHINA is called (   ) rice.

EXERCISE 5

Use ONE of the following words to complete each sentence. (Between; at; for; from; among; over

1. The horse jumped .... the hurdle.
2. The woman showed no regards .... his feelings.
3. Tom had to sit .... the two girls.

27

4. He was told to aim .... the target.
5. Your house is different .... mine.
6. They shared the apples .... the three boys.

Write down the word in each group which RHYMES with the one in capitals.

7. SCENE. Dream; scream; clean; feign; seem.
8. FABLE. Table; feeble; entail; legible; audible.
9. COARSE. Terse; Hoarse; first; fleece; grease.
10. FAINT. Clear; sane; reign; paint; train.
11. HOLLOW. Grotto; Bellow; borrow; yellow; follow.
12. STEER. Steal; clear; steel; plain; appeal.

Write down a word which describes the word *in italics* in each sentence, and formed from the word in brackets on the same line. One is done for you:—

(WIDTH). Explorers often have to cross wide *rivers*.

13. (NOISE) There was a .... *meeting* in the new hall.
14. (STRENGTH) The .... *man* lifted the heavy bag.
15. (CRUELTY) Nero was a .... *emperor*.
16. (PLEASE) We spent a .... *holiday* in Paris.
17. (FAME) Nelson was a .... *admiral*.
18. (ATTRACT) She was a very .... *girl*.

In each of these sentences, the words *in italics* can be replaced by ONE word, without affecting the meaning of the sentence. One is done for you.

The *man who sells papers, pens and pencils* is leaving. (Stationer).

19. The *man who controlled the football match* was unpopular.

28

20. The river ran in the *lowland between two hills*.
21. The old man had lived for nearly a *hundred years*.
22. We passed the *field full of fruit trees*.
23. The *man who looks after the prisoners in gaol* is retiring.
24. The *man who hid on the ship* was caught.

Read the following passage from 'ROBINSON CRUSOE', and then answer the questions below:—

It happened about noon, going towards my boat, I was exceedingly surprised with the print of a man's naked foot on the shore, which was very plain to be seen on the sand.

I stood like one thunderstruck, or as if I had seen an apparition. I listened, looking around me, I could hear nothing, nor see anything.

I went up to the rising ground to look farther. I went up the shore and down the shore, but I could see no other impressions but that one.

From 'ROBINSON CRUSOE'
by Daniel Defoe.

25. How many footprints did Crusoe see? (One; two; three; four).
26. Which word means nearly the same as APPARITION? (Apparatus; apparent; ghost; native).
27. Why did Crusoe go to the rising ground? (to inspect the boat; to look farther; to take exercise; to look for more prints).
28. Which word means nearly the same as THUNDER-STRUCK? (Shocked; apparent; hurt; frightened).
29. Where was Crusoe going at the time he found the print? (Up the hill; up the shore; to the boat; down the shore).

30. Which word is used instead of PRINT in the passage? (Mark; foot; impression; plain).
31. At what time did he notice the print? (Tea-time; morning; afternoon; noon).
32. Which of these is the OPPOSITE of RISING GROUND? (Falling ground; level ground; steep ground; flat ground).

In each of these words, letters are missing. Write out the word in full. One is done for you.

S**ZE (EI)

33. SH**LD
34. BEL**VE
35. REC**PT
36. F**RCE
37. Y**LD
38. DEC**VE

Write down the correct form of the verb. One is done for you.

Each of the boys (have; has) a bicycle. (has).

39. Not one of the players (was; were) injured.
40. (Is; are) any of your sisters married?
41. Only one of the cars (was; were) damaged.
42. (Is; are) either of your brothers going to school?
43. None of the small boats (was; were) sunk in the storm.
44. He (have; has) not been away long.

From this list of words, select ONE that is OPPOSITE to the word *in italics*.

Few; sober; expensive; hate; bright; haughty.

45. One coat was *cheap* but the other was (   ).
46. There were *many* passengers but (   ) were injured.
47. One man was *drunk*; the others were (   ).

30

48. Tom is a *dull* boy but his sister is (   ).
49. I (   ) skating but I *love* dancing.
50. One lady was *humble*; the other was (   ).

The word BULL is MASCULINE GENDER. The FEMININE GENDER of BULL is COW. Write down the FEMININE gender of the word in capitals.
51. My friend is a BACHELOR (   ).
52. Her NEPHEW (   ) is going away tomorrow.
53. The BRIDEGROOM (   ) seemed very nervous.
54. The COLT (   ) was grazing in the meadow.
55. A RAM (   ) was caught in the thicket.
56. The WAITER (   ) was most attentive.

Read these sentences:—(*a*) TODAY I SEE. (*b*) YESTERDAY I SAW. The word ' SAW ' is the PAST tense of the word ' SEE '.
In each of the following sentences, change TODAY to YESTERDAY and make any necessary changes in the VERB *in italics*.
57. TODAY I *sing* at the concert.
58. TODAY I *speak* at the meeting.
59. TODAY I *drink* a bottle of milk
60. TODAY I *ride* my bicycle to school.
61. TODAY the teacher *rings* the bell.
62. TODAY I *go* to school by bus.

In each group of words there is ONE word that is different from the others. Which is it?
63. Gold; slate; silver; copper; tin.
64. Beech; elm; oak; tulip; fir; eucalyptus.
65. Cairo; Nairobi; Glasgow; Edinburgh; Valletta.

66. Dagger; gun; pistol; revolver; rifle.
67. Oil; water; petrol; linen; milk.
68. Buff; pink; green; yellow; shade.
Use the conjunctions ' AND ' or ' BUT ' to join these sentences:—
69. The knight is bold .... the prince is timid.
70. My feet are cold .... my hands are warm.
71. It snowed yesterday .... it is snowing again today.
72. Lucy has fair hair .... so has her sister.
73. I slipped on the pavement .... I was not hurt.
74. Father went to the circus .... I went too.

Write down the name of the homes of the following:—
75. A Minister lives in a (   ).
76. A prisoner lives in a (   ).
77. An Eskimo lives in an (   ).
78. A bee lives in a (   ).
79. A vicar lives in a (   ).
80. A gypsy lives in a (   ).

Certain words are often used in pairs. Here is a list of such ' doubles ':—
   Spick and span; on and off; fits and starts; again and again; hammer and tongs; rack and ruin.
Use ONE of the above ' doubles ' in each of these sentences.
81. He tried .... and .... to remember.
82. Mary likes to keep her house .... and ....
83. It was raining .... and .... all day.
84. Her business is going to .... and ....
85. The fighters went at it .... and ....
86. This engine goes by .... and ....

32

Read this passage and then answer the questions that follow:—

The sun began to sink in the west. The fowls gathered round pecking here and there at the morsels of biscuit which had fallen on the ground. Then my wife produced the bag she had so mysteriously huddled into the tub, and drawing from it handfuls of grain scattered them upon the ground for the ducks and hens.

Seeing this, I suggested that we should not use anything so valuable so lavishly, but keep it as seed for a future harvest, in which she agreed. Then the pigeons sought a roosting place among the rocks; the hens ranged themselves in a line along the ridge of the tent; and the geese and the ducks betook themselves in a body, cackling and quacking as they proceeded to a marshy bit of ground near the sea, where some thick bushes offered them shelter.

From ' SWISS FAMILY ROBINSON '
by M. WYSS.

87. To what part of the day does the writer refer? (Morning; afternoon; noon; evening).

88. What was in the bag? (Bread; grain; biscuits; bones).

89. Where was the marshy ground situated? (Near the sea; in the field; on the hill; in the valley).

90. Which word means nearly the same as LAVISHLY? (Carelessly; foolishly; generously; scarcely).

91. Which word means nearly the same as ' In a body '? (One by one; in pairs; one behind the other; all together).

92. Which birds sought shelter in the bushes? (Pigeons; ducks and geese; hens).

33

93. Which word is OPPOSITE to 'Shelter'? (Sleep; expose; stay; live).
94. What is a MORSEL of biscuit? (A small piece; a very small piece; a medium piece; a large piece).

In the last exercise we read that the Hens CACKLED; the ducks QUACKED. Add suitable verbs (sound words) to the following.

95. The horse ....   96. The lark....................
97. The hound ....   98. The mouse..............
99. The donkey................   100. The cat ....

EXERCISE 6

Write down a word that can be used instead of the words *in italics* in the sentence.
1. The guard waved his flag and blew *the guard's* whistle.
2. The dog failed to catch the hare as *the hare* was too fast.
3. The old man gave the girl a pound, for which *the girl* was grateful.
4. The detective searched the building but *the detective* failed to find the jewels.
5. My friend and I are going on holiday and *my friend and I* hope to enjoy it.
6. I met Jim and Joe at the fair and joined *Jim and Joe*.

Write down the correct word in these sentences:—
7. I asked him if (is; his) father was coming.
8. (His; is) mother has gone away for a week.
9. I didn't know that he had lost (is; his) watch.

34

10. Every time he calls, he (his; is) late.
11. Each of the girls (as; has) a doll.
12. All but John (are; is) going to the show.

From the given clues, complete these adjectives connected with the words *in italics*. They all end in ' ful'.

13. If you *succeed* you are s******ful.
14. If you are *not sure* of something, you are d****ful.
15. A crane that *lifts heavy loads* is p****ful.
16. A person who *does not tell lies* is t****ful.
17. An article that can be *used for many purposes* is u**ful.
18. A person who drives *with caution* is c***ful.

Complete the following:—

19. PIG is to STY as .... is to STABLE.
20. GREEN is to COLOUR as GREENGAGE is to ....
21. MILK is to LIQUID as BUTTER is to............
22. WATER is to DRINK as BREAD is to ....
23. TEACHER is to SCHOOL as NURSE is to ....
24. DOWN is to UP as .... is to HIGH.

Write down the word that is related to the name in capitals:—

25. MARCONI. Traveller; inventor; soldier; missionary.
26. NELSON. Admiral; Ship; general; explorer.
27. WORDSWORTH. Author; teacher; poet; writer.
28. Capt. COOK. Editor; Doctor; Scientist; Explorer.
29. CHARLES DICKENS. Poet; journalist; author; inventor.
30. KITCHENER. Chef; soldier; statesman; sailor.

Read the following passage and then answer the questions below.

Sunday always began with a Bible story, followed by a breakfast of baked beans, which two things were much tangled up together in Ohilly's mind.

After breakfast the children studied their Sunday-school lessons, and then the big carry-all came round, and they drove to church, which was a good mile off.

It was a large, old-fashioned church, with galleries, and long pews with high red-cushioned seats. The choir sat at the end, behind a low, green curtain, which slipped from side to side on rods. When the sermon began, they would draw aside the curtain and show themselves, all ready to listen, but the rest of the time they kept it shut.

Katy always guessed that they must be having a good time behind the green curtain—eating orange-peel, perhaps, or reading the Sunday book—and she often wished she might sit up there among them.

From ' WHAT KATY DID '
by S. Coolidge.

31. How far did Katy live from the church? (About two miles; about one mile; near-by).
32. What is a ' Carry-all '? (A large basket; a hamper; a vehicle; a suitcase).
33. What were the long pews? (Curtains; chairs; stools; seats).
34. At what part of the service did they show themselves? (At the beginning; throughout; during the sermon; at the end).
35. What is meant by ' tangled-up '? (Mixed; fastened; loosened; tied).

36. Write a word that sounds the same as GUESSED, but is spelt differently.
37. Form an adjective from the word BIBLE.
38. What two colours are mentioned in the story?

Select two words from the list below and join them to make a new word. Complete this by joining six pairs of words.

    Mill; jam; cup; butter; cloth; wife; pot; egg; pond; floor; house; fly.

39.   40.
41.   42.
43.   44.

Write down the correct word in each bracket:
45. The camels travelled across the (desert; dessert).
46. I watched the lambs (gamble; gambol) in the meadow.
47. She had a (bare, bear) as a pet.
48. The (quay; key) to the cupboard is lost.
49. I was dazzled by the (raise; rays) of the sun.
50. We use a (plain; plane) in the woodwork class.

Here is a list of CONTAINERS:—Barrel; envelope; caddy; vase; wardrobe; creel.
Write down the container that holds the following:—
51. Tea (   ).   52. Fish (   ).
53. Beer (   ).   54. Flowers (   ).
55. Letters (   ).   56. Clothes (   ).

Complete each of these PROVERBS by adding the last word:—
57. A miss is as good as a ....
58. Better late than ....

59. Exchange is no ....
60. More haste, less ....
61. Once bitten, twice ....
62. All that glitters is not ....

Rearrange these groups of words to form a sentence:—
63. Make; we; bread; flour; from
64. Jug; milk; the; in; the; is
65. Oranges; made; is; marmalade; from
66. Flesh; is; mutton; the; sheep; a; of; called.
67. Is; children; milk; for; good
68. Blackboard; on; Tommy; wrote; the

Write down a VERB formed from the word in capitals:—
69. MARRIAGE. Fred and Mary intend to (   ) next year.
70. LOSS. Mother told me not to (   ) the money.
71. CHOICE. I did not know which hat to (   ).
72. BELIEF. The teacher would not (   ) that the boy was ill.
73. BEAUTY. Advertisements do not always (   ) the countryside.
74. THRIFT. His business will not (   ) unless he takes more interest in it.

Read the following passage and then answer the questions that follow:—

On and on, beneath the dewy darkness, they fled swiftly down the swirling stream; underneath black walls, and temples and the castles of the princes of the East; past fragrant gardens and groves of all strange fruits; past marshes where fat kine lay sleeping, and long beds of whispering reeds; till they heard the merry music of the surge upon the bar, as it tumbled in the moonlight all alone.

Into the surge they rushed, and ' Argo ' leapt the breakers like a horse; for she knew the time was come to show her mettle, and win honour for the heroes and herself. Into the surge they rushed, and ' Argo ' leapt the breakers like a horse, till the heroes stopped, all panting, each man upon his oar, as she slid into the still broad sea.

Then Orpheus took his harp and sang, till the heroes' hearts rose high again; and they rowed on stoutly and steadfastly, away into the darkness of the west.

From ' THE HEROES '
—Charles Kingsley,

75. What is the meaning of FRAGRANT? (Pretty; beautiful; sweet-smelling).
76. What is the meaning of KINE? (Cattle; sheep, horses; goats).
77. By what was the Argo driven? (Steam; oars; sails; oil).
78. In which direction was the Argo travelling? (North; south; east; west).
79. What part of the day is described? (Morning; noon; dawn: night).
80. What was the ' Merry music ' that the Heroes heard? (Orpheus playing the harp; Sound of the waves; Boatmen singing).
81. What word sounds the same as METTLE but is spelt differently?
82. Write in the PRESENT TENSE:—She SLID into the broad sea. ....

All the words with letters missing end in ' son '. Write each word out:—

83. A small purple fruit is called a ***son.
84. Spring is the first ***son of the year.
85. He did not give a ***son for his action.
86. The judge sentenced him to ***son.
87. If you drink ***son, you may die.
88. I have a music ***son every Saturday.

The word ' Isn't ' is a short form of writing ' Is not '. Read the following and write the short form of the words *in italics*:—

89. I told him that I *had not* been at the concert.
90. *I am* not certain that I am going to the show.
91. David *could not* play on Tuesday.
92. I *do not* know if we are going to the match.
93. I told him that it *did not* matter.
94. Peter *will not* join in any of the games.

We speak of a small quantity of water as a DROP of water. Write down a word meaning a small quantity of the following:—

95. A .... of dust.   96. A .... of salt.
97. A .... of smoke.   98. A .... of butter.
99. A .... of sand.   100. A .... of wind.

EXERCISE 7

Write down ONE word to complete the sentence:—

1. The huntsman went in pursuit .... the fox.
2. When I cracked the vase, my father was angry .... me.
3. The clock fell .... the mantelpiece.

4. Jane said she saw him walking .... the window.
5. The postman was standing .... the pillar box.
6. The prisoner sat .... the two warders.

This sentence can be written in two ways:—
   (*a*) The man shot the rabbit.
   (*b*) The rabbit was shot by the man.
Both sentences mean the same. Now write each of these
sentences like the second one, so that the meaning is
not changed.
   7. The cat caught a little bird.
   8. The gardener grew some roses.
   9. The tramp frightened the boy.
10. The patient drank the medicine.
11. The operator showed two films.
12. The pilot flew the new plane.

Write down a NOUN formed from the word in capitals:—
13. SELECT. There was a good (   ) of sweets in the
       shop.
14. ADVERTISE. I saw the (   ) in the local paper.
15. DARK. I crept up to the house as (   ) fell.
16. DEEP. Doris was not aware of the (   ) of the
       water.
17. VAIN. The woman's (   ) made her unpopular.
18. SUCCEED. His (   ) has gone to his head.

Complete each of these sentences:—
19. The athlete was as fit as a ....
20. The twins were as like as ....
21. I was as pleased as .... with my present.
22. The accused claimed that he was as sober as a
       ....

41

23. The two men were as thick as ....
24. He was walking to school as slow as a ....

Give one name for:—
25. Three persons singing together.
26. A stand with three legs.
27. A three sided figure.
28. Four persons singing together.
29. A three wheeled cycle.
30. A period of one hundred years.

What is the correct word here?
31. The girl waded (to; too; two) far into the water.
32. One or (to; too; two) people lost the bus.
33. I hope (to; too; two) go to school on Monday.
34. John waved to me (has; as) he passed.
35. His work (as; has) never been finished.
36. As soon (as; has) the phone rings, I will call you.

The SOUND of a drum is called the BEAT of a drum.
Write the sound made by the following:—
37. The .... of a trumpet.
38. The .... of a motor horn.
39. The .... of a clock.
40. The .... of a motor engine.
41. The .... of a bow.
42. The .... of a telephone.

Write down a word which is similar in meaning
to the one on the left, and rhymes with the one on the
right.
43. Amazement   (   )   Thunder
44 Loyal   (   )   Blue.

42

45. Circular   (   )   Ground.
46. Minimum   (   )   Feast.
47. Option   (   )   Voice.
48. Candid   (   )   Bank.

Read the following passage and then answer the questions below:—

The Phantom, slowly, gravely, silently approached. When it came near him, Scrooge bent down upon his knee, for in the very air through which this Spirit moved, it seemed to scatter gloom and mystery.

It was shrouded in a deep black garment, which concealed its head, its face, its form, and left nothing of it visible save one outstretched hand.

But for this it would have been difficult to detach its figure from the night, and separate it from the darkness by which it was surrounded.

He felt that it was tall and stately when it came beside him, and that its mysterious presence filled him with a solemn dread.

He knew no more, for the Spirit neither moved nor spoke. " I am in the presence of the Ghost of Christmas Yet to Come? " said Scrooge.

The Spirit answered not, but pointed onward with its hand.

From ' CHRISTMAS CAROL '
by Charles Dickens.

49. What does the word ' Garment ' mean? (Shoes; clothes; sandals; socks).
50. What is the meaning of ' Silently approached '? (Asked a question; came nearer; went away; stood still).

51. What is the meaning of 'To scatter gloom'? (To spread happiness; to cheer; to praise; to spread sadness).
52. What other word is used instead of PHANTOM?
53. Which of these parts of the Phantom could be seen? (Its face; its hand; its form; its feet).
54. What word could have been used instead of *solemn*? (Sad; cheerful; lonely; fearful).
55. Form a NOUN from GRAVE.
56. Form a VERB from KNEE.

Write down ONE word that could be used instead of the words *in italics*.
57. The boy was thrashed *without mercy*.
58. The nurse watched the patient *with anxiety*.
59. He set the trap *with cunning*.
60. The pilot attacked the target *without fear*.
61. When the ship was struck, the crew left *with haste*.
62. The porter was asked to handle the luggage *with care*.

Which is more correct here—either ' and ' or ' but '?
63. I tried to carry the box .... it was too heavy.
64. The goalkeeper dived to the left .... saved the shot.
65. Janet tried to catch the bus .... she was too late.
66. The road was frosty .... the cyclist skidded.
67. The guard waved his flag .... the train started.
68. Father likes football .... mother isn't interested.

Write down the word in each group which is OPPOSITE in meaning to the word on the left:—
69. ABSENCE. Reply; presence; return; journey; safety.

44

70. DEPART. Stay; going; leave; arrive; start.
71. BETTER. Well; good; fit; worse; improve.
72. EASY. Difficult; tranquil; nice; simple; dear.
73. INNOCENT. Daring; careful; useful; guilty; tried.
74. TRUE. False; candid; successful; curious; cute.

Write these ABBREVIATIONS in full:—
75. B.C.   76. J.P.
77. M.P.   78. R.A.F.
79. Ltd.   80. C.O.D.

Write down the words in each sentence which should
have a capital letter:—
81. we passed through cardiff on our way to london.
82. last tuesday i met my aunt at the station.
83. my brother will have a holiday in june.
84. tom smith is my best friend.
85. my mother told me that i could stay home on
    friday.
86. most of the shops in high street were closed.

Read this poem and then answer the questions below:—
   " Waken lords and ladies gay,
       On the mountain dawns the day;
       All the jolly chase is here
       With hawk and horse and hunting spear.
       Hounds are in their couples yelling,
       Hawks are whistling, horns are knelling,
       Merrily, merrily mingle they,
       Waken lords and ladies gay."

   Waken, lords and ladies gay,
   To the greenwood haste away;

We can show where he lies,
Fleet of foot and tall of size;
We can show the marks he made
When 'gainst the oak his antlers frayed;
You shall see him brought to bay;
" Waken lords and ladies gay."

Sir WALTER SCOTT.

87. At what time of day did the chase meet? (Dawn; midday; dusk; evening).
88. What animal is being hunted? (Rabbits; foxes; deer; otters).
89. Which three words tell us that the animal could run fast?
90. Name three creatures engaged in the hunt.
91. What made the marks on the oak tree?
92. Write another word that means MINGLE.
93. Form an adjective from MOUNTAIN.
94. What word could have been used instead of ' Haste away'?

———————

Write down the PAST TENSE of the verb in the bracket. One is done for you.

I KEPT my money in a purse. (Keep).

95. He was so strong that he .... the iron bar. (Bend).
96. The wound in his leg .... for a long time. (Bleed).
97. We .... in prayer at the altar. (Kneel).
98. My mother .... the milkman yesterday. (Pay).
99. We all .... quietly towards the window. (Creep).
100. The man .... still while the funeral passed. (Stand).

46

EXERCISE 8

Name the NOUNS in each sentence:—
1. The girl has a pet rabbit.
2. The duchess has five servants.
3. I bought the tablets from the chemist.
4. Water was leaking from the hole in the tube.
5. I left my pen on the desk in the classroom.
6. The conductress punched the ticket and gave it to the passenger.

Name the correct PRONOUN in each bracket:—
7. Peter gave the oranges to (We; us).
8. Tom is taller than (Me; I).
9. Neither Jack nor (he; him) had heard the story.
10. (Us; we) don't know who is responsible.
11. My father gave (me; I) five pence.
12. Both Pamela and (she; her) attend the classes.

In the word CALM the letter ' L ' is silent. Write a word with a silent letter to complete each sentence:—
13. A baker has to .... the dough before baking.
14. The frost made my fingers feel quite ....
15. Parts of the .... vessel were washed up on the shore.
16. I failed to plane the wood owing to the .... in it.
17. I asked the shopkeeper to .... up the parcel.
18. The mouse .... the cheese.

In each group, write down the word that names the CLASS to which the others belong. One is done for you.
   Cabbage; potatoes; carrots; (vegetables); turnips.
19. Lion; tiger; giraffe; zebra; animal.
20. Canary; bird; robin; sparrow; swallow.

21. Bee; wasp; beetle; insect; fly.
22. Season; autumn; spring; summer; winter.
23. Lorry; car; vehicle; omnibus; van.
24. Smell; sense; taste; feel; hear.

What is the correct word in the brackets?
25. The (pane; pain) of glass was cracked.
26. Irene was late and (mist; missed) the train.
27. The referee gave a free kick for the (fowl; foul).
28. I put the (sealing; ceiling) wax on the letter.
29. The (male; mail) train arrived ten minutes late.
30. Alice is going to change the (stile; style) of her hair.

Read the following and then answer the questions that follow:—

At length, after several days fatiguing journey over mountains and plains, the party with which Martin travelled, arrived at the Indian village.

Here the warriors were received with the utmost joy by the wives and children whom they had left behind, and for a long time Martin was left almost entirely to do as he pleased.

A few days before, his bonds had been removed, and once or twice he thought of attempting to escape; but whenever he wandered a little farther than usual into the woods, he found that he was watched and followed by a tall and powerful savage, whose duty it evidently was to see that the prisoner did not escape.

'MARTIN RATTLER'
by R. M. Ballantyne.

31. What does FATIGUING mean? (Long; tiring; awful; fearful).

32. When were Martin's bonds removed? (Before he arrived; after he arrived; when he arrived).
33. Who welcomed the warriors?
34. What word could be used instead of ATTEMPTING?
35. What word is the *opposite* to ESCAPE?
36. Who was watching Martin?
37. Give another word that could be used instead of ENTIRELY?
38. To where did Martin wander?

Here is a list of words that can be used when asking questions:—
   When; where; how; what; why; which.
Use one of the above words to complete these questions:—
39. " .... are you today," asked Mr. Jones.
40. .... are you going to call again?
41. .... did the suite cost?
42. .... of these two cars do you prefer?
43. .... does Mrs. Green live?
44. .... do you dislike his company.

Write down the correct word in each of the brackets:—
45. Please get (of; off) the chair.
46. One (off; of) my hands is dirty.
47. I took this book from (off; of) the shelf.
48. It looks as though (its; It's) going to snow.
49. The dog ran into (it's; its) kennel.
50. (It's; its) no use crying about it.

Write out the following sentences, putting in the punctuation marks shown, where necessary:— . , " ?
51. Where did you buy your bicycle asked Harry

52. Did you remember to do your homework asked the teacher
53. The train stopped at Cardiff Hereford Shrewsbury and Crewe
54. I asked Jim if he was going
55. My new box of paints contained red blue green yellow and brown.
56. What time is it asked Jane I replied it is ten oclock

———————

Write out a word that rhymes with the word on the left:—

Word	Col. 1	Col. 2
57. Fairy	M....................	d ....
58. Range	c	s ....
59. Whistle	t	b ....
60. Plumb	c	n ....
61. Dreary	w......................	c ....
62. Suite	t	w ....

———————

Write the name for MORE THAN ONE (Plural) of the following:—
63. Brother-in-law
64. Cupful
65. Man-of-war
66. Passer-by
67. Spoonful
68. Mouse-trap.

———————

Write down the FEMININE gender of the word *in italics*.
69. The *lion* and the .... were resting in the cage.
70. The *landlord* and the .... were present at the party.

71. Frank has two rabbits, a *buck* and a ....
72. The farmer sold the *bullock* and the ....
73. I saw a *friar* and a .... in the street.
74. The *earl* and the .... live near me.

Read this very carefully:—

Tom Brown married Jane Green and had two children Fred and Mary. Fred married Anne White and they too, had two children Frank and Irene. Mary married Joe Black and they had a daughter Lucy, and two sons, Jim and Peter. Here is a diagram of the family:—

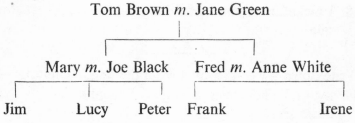

Tom Brown *m*. Jane Green

Mary *m*. Joe Black   Fred *m*. Anne White

Jim   Lucy   Peter   Frank   Irene

75. What relation is Tom Brown to Frank? (Father; grandfather; brother; uncle).
76. What relation is Lucy to Jane? (Grandmother; niece; grandchild; daughter).
77. What relation is Peter to Fred? (Son; cousin; son-in-law; nephew).
78. What relation is Anne to Jane? (Daughter-in-law; niece; daughter; aunt).
79. What relation is Mary to Anne? (Cousin; aunt; sister-in-law; sister).
80. Who is Frank's uncle? (Tom; Joe; Fred; Jim).

81. What relation is Lucy to Irene? (Cousin; niece; sister; aunt).
82. How many grandchildren have Tom and Jane? (One; two; three; four; five).

Complete these 'doubles':—
83. This engine has had a lot of WEAR and ....
84. He expects me to be at his BECK and ....
85. I was pleased to know he had arrived SAFE and ....
86. I looked HIGH and .... for the lost dog.
87. The policeman put the burglar under LOCK and ....
88. I picked up some useful ODDS and .... at the sale.

Write down a word formed from the one in capitals:—
89. FAULT. There was a .... connection in the radio set.
90. LIVE. We had a .... discussion on the subject.
91. ANXIETY. It was an .... moment for the doctor.
92. GOLD. The .... corn was waving in the field.
93. PATIENT. The nurse showed great .... with the girl.
94. QUARREL. Richard seemed a rather .... boy.

Use the prefixes:—'in'; 'un'; 'il' to form a word OPPOSITE in meaning to the following words:—
95. Legal   96. Common
97. Audible   98. Legible
99. Tidy   100. Correct

EXERCISE 9

Write down ONE of the following words to complete the sentence:—

To; against; of; with; upon; among.

1. In defiance .... the captain's orders, the boy left the field.
2. Bill Smith bears a strong resemblance .... his father.
3. The visitors protested .... the charge for the meal.
4. My mother prevailed .... my friend to stay.
5. The girl shared the sweets .... her friends.
6. I was disgusted .... his behaviour.

Write down a word that means the same or nearly the same as the one on the left, and rhymes with the one on the right.

The first one is done for you:—

Abode .... (dwelling) .... swelling.

7. Conversation .... (................) ....chalk.
8. Cunning .... (................) .... why.
9. Maximum .... (................) ....ghost.
10. Assemble .... (................) .... father.
11. Insane .... (................) .... glad.
12. Caution .... (................) .... share.

Write the word in the bracket that is opposite to the one *in italics*.

13. This box is *full* but the other is (locked; open; empty; keyed).
14. Tom was *early*, but Jane was (present; late; absent; gone).

53

15. I *often* meet her, but (sometimes; never; always; seldom) speak to her.
16. One boy was *quiet*, but the others were (noisy; sulky; talking; still).
17. He painted the *interior* of the hall and will do the (top; ceiling; outside; inside) later.
18. The critic *condemned* one act, but (sentenced; praised; invited; enquired) the other.

Complete the following sentences:—
19. I felt as SICK as a ....
20. The little boy was as CUNNING as a ....
21. This box is as HEAVY as ....
22. The servant was as STUBBORN as a ....
23. The princess was as PROUD as a ....
24. I was told to keep as QUIET as a ....

Read the following story and answer the questions that follow.

The Two Houses

Now, the garden separated the Marches' house from that of Mr. Laurence. Both stood in a suburb of the city, which was still country-like, with groves and lawns, large gardens and quiet streets.

A low hedge parted the two estates. On one side was an old, brown house, looking rather bare and shabby, robbed of the vines that in summer covered its walls, and the flowers which then surrounded it.

On the other side was a stately stone mansion. plainly betokening every sort of comfort and luxury, from the big coach house and well-kept grounds to the conservatory and the glimpses of lovely things one caught between the rich curtains.

54

Yet is seemed a lonely, lifeless sort of house; for no children frolicked on the lawn, no motherly face ever smiled at the windows, and few people went in and out except the old gentleman and his grandson.

From ' LITTLE WOMEN '

L. M. ALCOTT.

25. What separated the two houses? (A low hedge; the estate; a garden; a mansion).
26. Which building is referred to as lonely? (The Marches' house; Mr. Laurence's house; the mansion; the brown house).
27. Why was the brown house bare? (It had not been painted; the vines and flowers were missing; it was untenanted; it was old).
28. Where is a suburb situated? (Somewhere inside a city; on the fringe; a long way off; in the centre).
29. What was between the two estates? (A low hedge; groves and lawns; a quiet street; a large garden).
30. Which word is nearly the same as LUXURY? (Poverty; riches; happiness; prosperous).
31. Of what material was the mansion built? (Brick; slate; stone; asbestos).
32. What word could be used instead of GLIMPSE? (Glimmer; glow; taste; sight).

Write the correct form of the VERB IN CAPITALS.

33. FALL. The boy has .... off his bicycle.
34. TRY. Bill .... his best, but failed.
35. WEAR. I haven't .... that suit for a week.
36. GO. Nesta has .... to the shop for her mother.
37. FLY. The robin .... through the window.
38. BREAK. Jean .... her leg while skating.

Here are six words with the letters rearranged. The word in the bracket is similar in meaning to the word on the same line. Write the word by putting the letters in their correct order:—

39. A H P Y P means (gay)
40. K S E P A means (talk)
41. O C R R T E C means (right)
42. A T R P D E means (leave)
43. G N E O H U means (sufficient)
44. U G H E means (very big)

Here are twelve small words. Join them in pairs to form six new words:—

Man; ache; foot; board; ball; hood; black; coal; cup; tooth; house; tea.

45.   46.   47.
48.   49   50.

Write ONE word which means the same as the following:
51. A place for storing a car.
52. Children on the register of a school.
53. A fertile spot in a desert.
54. A small stream joining a river.
55. A step on a ladder.
56. A doctor who performs operations.

Find the ADJECTIVE (describing word) in each sentence.
57. The mountainous waves crashed against the rocks.
58. It was a starry night when I went for a walk.
59. I slept in a comfortable bed at the hotel.
60. The injured driver was feeling ill.
61. I gave the baby a plastic doll.
62. We spent a night in the haunted house.

In each of these sentences, there is a word that has a SILENT letter. Find it.

63. I put the money in the palm of her hand.
64. The vicar read the psalm in church.
65. My sister is knitting a pullover for me.
66. Joan helped her mother wring the clothes.
67. The body of Jesus was laid in the tomb.
68. The worm wriggled when I touched it.

Write down each word in the sentences which should have a capital letter:

69. the nile flows through egypt.
70. nairobi is the capital of kenya.
71. i was fourteen last thursday.
72. we sail from liverpool on the queen elizabeth on june 14th.
73. the israelites crossed the red sea.
74. prince philip is very popular.

A collection of sheep is called a FLOCK. Write down the COLLECTIVE NOUNS in the following sentences.

75. A .... of musicians strolled down our street.
76. He dreamed that a .... of angels appeared.
77. Farmers used to plough with a .... of horses.
78. My father is on the .... of directors.
79. A .... of insects destroyed the apple blossom.
80. We found a .... of rabbits in the field.

Here is a short story from which certain words are missing. Read the story and think of a suitable word to make the story complete and sensible:

81. As I was .... down the road,
82. I .... a strange looking
83. man carrying a small .... in his

57

84. left hand. It was brown in ....
85. and had a metal .... which he
86. held tightly. He was lame and ....
87. along slowly. His face was .... with
88. wrinkles, and he looked far from ....

Write down a NOUN formed from the word in brackets:—
89. We watched the .... of the train from the station. (depart).
90. At the .... of the game. we all caught a bus. (conclude).
91. Most people detest .... to animals. (cruel).
92. A lion is noted for its .... when fighting. (ferocious).
93. It is always better to tell the .... (true).
94. .... is always better than cure. (prevent).

In each group of words, there is ONE which means the same or nearly the same as the word in capitals. Write it down.
95. AFFECTIONATE. affected; effective; loving; hostile.
96. BLAMED. cursed; accused; tried; encouraged.
97. LOFTY. tall; above; over; under.
98. JOIN. enjoy; gather; connect; disperse.
99. INSOLENT. innocent; watchful; guilty; rude.
100. MARGIN. separate; edge; corner; middle.

EXERCISE 10

In each sentence, write ONE of these words:
Before; after; if; because; so; although.
1. I hope to go to the party .... it does not rain.

2. .... I feel tired, I will try to finish it tonight.
3. I may call on you tonight .... I have had my tea.
4. He went to bed early .... he was feeling tired.
5. I washed and dressed .... I had my breakfast.
6. I did not feel like going .... I decided to stay at home.

Instead of the words *in italics*, write ONE word which means the same:—
7. The good news made me jump *with excitement*.
8. The people bowed their heads *in respect* as the cortege passed.
9. My father tackled the problem *with every confidence*.
10. Irene drove the new car *with ease*.
11. The mechanic adjusted the points *with skill*.
12. The witness left the court *in a hurry*.

Write the following abbreviations in full:-
13. Esq.   14. p.s.
15. P.T.O.   16. L.B.W.
17. I.O.U.   18. a.m.

Complete these proverbs:—
19. A stitch in time ....
20. New brooms ....
21. Let sleeping dogs ....
22. Too many cooks ....
23. Empty vessels ....
24. It's never too late ....

59

Which is the correct word in the bracket?
25. A convict lives in a (home; hospital; prison; flat).
26. A nun lives in a (monastery; rectory; manse; convent).
27. A soldier lives in a (caravan; barracks; house; factory).
28. A beaver lives in a (lodge; nest; hutch; lair).
29. A sheep lives in a (stable; shed; pen; byre).
30. A hen lives in a (sty; shed; nest; coop).

We speak of ONE dog but MORE THAN ONE *dogs*.
The word DOG is SINGULAR number. The word DOGS is PLURAL number. Write the PLURAL number of the word *in italics*.
31. The *child* (   ) felt happy at the picnic.
32. I watched the men repairing the *roof*. (   ).
33. The spider was watching the *fly*. (   ).
34. The girl was too short to reach the *shelf*. (   ).
35. The mark of Tommy's *foot* (   ) showed clearly.
36. The mothers seemed interested in the *baby*. (   ).

The sentence (*a*) is written in another way at (*b*) without changing the meaning.
  (*a*) The bull *chased* the farmer.
  (*b*) The farmer *was chased by* the bull.
Write each of these sentences in the same way as the one above at (*b*).
37. The clumsy hen broke the eggs.
38. The falling tree damaged the roof.
39. The horse threw the jockey.
40. The two boys stole the fruit.
41. The little girl upset the tea.
42. The nurse bandaged his arm.

Write down the word in each group which means the same as the one in capitals:—

43. TERRIBLE. Great; awful; rough; glamorous.
44. SMALL. Large; great; little; huge;
45. ODOUR. Clean; smell; offensive; touch.
46. INJURE. Harm; crush; crash; accident.
47. SOMETIMES. Always; occasionally; never; seldom.
48. ROOMY. Cool; wide; interior; spacious.

The passage below is part of a story, but some of the words have been omitted. Read it, and then suggest suitable words, so that it will make sensible reading.

49. In the .... I could hear a rumbling
50. noise like the .... of thunder.
51.   In a .... time, it started to rain
52. and soon it descended in ....
53.   I decided to .... under the nearest tree
54. until the rain had .... I had not been
55. there more than a .... minutes, when a
56. vivid .... of lightning scared me and I
    decided to hurry home.

Write one word which could be used instead of the words *in italics*:—

57. My *father's mother* is staying at our house.
58. My *sister's son* has won the competition.
59. His *mother's sister* gave him a present.
60. Her *sister's husband* is a keen cricketer.
61. His *brother's daughter* has started school.
62. My *father's sister* is a trained nurse.

All the following words end in ' fy'. The meaning of the word is given on the left. Complete each word:—
63. To make pure. ****fy

64. To bear witness. *****fy
65. To make beautiful. ******fy
66. To fill with terror. *****fy
67. To give notice to. ****fy
68. To make glorious. *****fy

Write out the correct word in each bracket:—
69. The (muscle; mussel) of his arm is sore.
70. The conductor told us to (paws; pause) at a certain note.
71. A (hoard; horde) of savages were yelling.
72. The doctor told me to avoid the (draught; draft).
73. I changed the (cheque; check) at the bank.
74. The bride wore a long white (vale; veil).

In each of the following sentences, name the VERB:—
75. We climbed the mountain very slowly.
76. All the boys played well.
77. Somebody threw a stone at the window.
78. The trouble started on the street corner.
79. We never expected a present from my uncle.
80. Please close the door.

Name the word in each group which is OPPOSITE to the one in capitals.
81. DIVIDE. Evade; multiply; subtract; add.
82. CONCEAL. Convene; seal; reveal; connect.
83. FERTILE. Barren; growing; seedling; futile.
84. NEVER. Often; sometimes; always; seldom.
85. SMOOTH. Track; course; flat; rough.
86. ANCIENT. Old; modern; anxious; old-fashioned.

Read the following and then answer the questions below.

Our Holiday

We were all very excited at the prospect of going to Margate for our holiday. We had arranged to leave our home town of Newport on the 9.0 a.m. train which is a non-stop express to Paddington, but the next train at 10.30 a.m. stops at Swindon and Reading.

My mother and my sister Ruth, who is twelve years old, were busy packing the cases, while father labelled them and made himself generally useful in other ways.

I am three years younger than my sister, so I was given the task of watching my baby brother John in case he crawled too near the fire. John is only two years of age, and calls me ' Di' as he cannot say Diane.

As the journey will take about five hours, we are taking sandwiches with us in case we are hungry on the train.

87. When were they going on holiday? (In a week's time; the next day; later on; that evening).

88. Why did they choose the 9.0 a.m. train? (Because it was a non-stop express; it was an early train; it was fast; it went through Paddington).

89. Who looked after the baby? (Father; mother; Diane; Ruth).

90. How old was Diane? (Two; nine; twelve; fifteen).

91. About what time do they expect to arrive at Margate? (1 p.m.; 2 p.m.; 3 p.m.; 4 p.m.).

92. How much older was Ruth than John? (3 years; 5 years; ten years; six years).

93. How many times does the 9.0 a.m. train stop

between Newport and Paddington? (Once; twice; none; three times).
94. How much older is Diane than John?   (5 years; 6 years; 7 years; 8 years).

Name the TWO words in each bracket that are PART OF or ASSOCIATED with the word in capitals.
95. FORK. (prongs; blade; meat; handle; eat).
96. FEET. (Waving; running; laughing; feeling; dancing).
97. HOUSE. (Cabin; tent; roof; walls; carriage).
98. PIANO. (Keys; singer; song; pedals; player).
99. WINDOW. (Seeing; glass; raise; pane; pain).
100. BIRD. (Boat; wings; beak; seed; grubs).

EXERCISE 11

In each sentence, write:—ON; OF or TO:—
1. The prisoner was found guilty .... manslaughter.
2. We finally agreed .... the date of the wedding.
3. The youngest boy was equal .... the others.
4. We tried to prevail .... the master to let us play.
5. Jim was the victim .... a vicious attack.
6. My hat is similar .... the one my friend wears.

Here are some punctuation marks:—(. , ? ! ”).
Punctuate these sentences using the correct marks from the above list.
7. May I leave now asked the boy
8. Larry enquired are you going home now
9. Hello exclaimed the policeman what are you doing
10. Miss Evans replied I cannot allow you to do so

11. Stop it shouted the little boy you will hurt me
12. I sowed carrots beet parsnips and lettuce in the garden

Write words that start with the letter given, and rhyme with the word in capitals.

13. SIMPLE. (d   ) (p   ).
14. ACHE. (sh   ) (st   ).
15. MUFF. (t   ) (en   ).
16. CURE. (f   ) (s   ).
17. CLEAR. (g   ) (b   ).
18. INCH. (p   ) (cl   ).

In each of these sentences, there is a word with missing letters. Write the word.

19. Mother spent two hours d**n**g my socks.
20. The jeweller examined the pr*c***s stones.
21. Some furniture is b**u*if*l*y made.
22. When I arrived, it was still r**n**g.
23. Sam is nervous; he is a*r**d in the dark.
24. We watched the sun sink below the ho**z*n.

Read the sentence at (*a*) and then the one at (*b*). In each the word SPRING is used, but its meaning is different. Now write a sentence at (*b*) using the word *in italics* in each sentence (*a*), so that it will have a different meaning from that in (*a*).

(*a*) I have broken the *spring* of my watch.

(*b*) I saw the dog *spring* at the man.

25. (*a*) Tom wore a hole in the *sole* of his shoe.

    (*b*) ....

26. (*a*) We planted some tulips in the *bowl*.

    (*b*) ....

27. The old clothes were stored in a *chest*.
    (b) ....

28. (*a*) The teacher asked Jane to *ring* the bell.
    (b) ....

29. (*a*) His team reached the third *round*.
    (b) ....

30. (*a*) We spent two hours at the *fair*.
    (b) ....

What is the correct form of the verb in each bracket?

31. Marjory (did; done) her best to win the prize.
32. This page is (tore; torn) who did it?
33. Peter thinks he (done; did) better than last time.
34. The teacher (torn; tore) the page out of the book.
35. Ann said, " I have (tore; torn) my dress.
36. After Jack had (did; done) his work, he watched television.

Name the word in each group which is OPPOSITE to the one in capitals:—

37. GIANT. Man; dwarf; child; actor.
38. LIGHT. Stout; grey; dark; high.
39. SWIFT. Speedy; fast; quick; slow.
40. SEIZE. Release; capture; catch; hold.
41. TOUGH. Leather; strong; tender; true.
42. HOSTILE. Friendly; happy; active; handy.

The word used to denote a COLLECTION of fish is a SHOAL of fish. Write the COLLECTIVE NOUN for each of the following:—

43. The hen and her .... of chickens crossed the road.
44. My father is on the .... of magistrates.

45. In the farmyard, we saw a .... of geese.
46. In the Bible, we read of a .... of locusts.
47. There was a meeting of the .... of directors.
48. A .... of labourers were working in the field.

The following small words can be joined in pairs to make a COMPOUND word, for example:—fly; paper = flypaper. Join the proper pairs to make SIX compound words:—

House; yard; life; ache; farm; craft; guard; dust; head; fly; pan; witch.

49.   50.   51.
52.   53.   54.

Read the following and then answer the questions that follow.

Today, when we wish to travel on land, we have the choice of railway, buses or cars, but in the days of our great grandparents, the most popular means of transport was by stage-coach.

This was drawn by horses, and mostly had to travel over poor, rough roads full of pot-holes and ruts which, in wet weather, were filled with water and the rest of the road was covered in thick mud. The horses, owing to the length of the journey, were changed at different places, and after being fed, were rested there until it was time for them to be used for another coach. Some passengers were obliged to travel outside the coach, and this could be extremely uncomfortable in the cold weather.

55. By what means did our great grandparents travel? (Train; bus; stage-coach; car).

56. When was the journey most pleasant? (Spring; summer; autumn; winter).
57. What were the roads like then? (Rough; tarred; wide; narrow).
58. Why were the horses changed? (They were too old; they were hungry; not fast enough; they were tired).
59. Which word could have been used instead of DRAWN? (Sketched; painted; pulled; rested).
60. What word means nearly the same as. EXTREMELY? (Never; very; stream; thick).
61. Why did some passengers travel outside? (Because they wished to; because there was no room inside; they wanted to view the scenery; it was colder).
62. What covered the roads in wet weather? (Snow; rain; mud; water).

———————

One word in each group is different in some way from all the others. Name the ODD word in each group.
63. Tea; bun; coffee; cocoa; milk.
64. Dandelion; daisy; elm; lily; primrose.
65. Cup; basin; plate; knife; saucer.
66. Trumpet; flute; banjo; solo; guitar.
67. Wife; bachelor; widower; uncle; husband.
68. Orange; turnip; plum; cherry; pear.

———————

Write down a NOUN formed from the word in brackets.
69. He was noted for his great .... (able).
70. There was a .... of goods on the stall. (various).
71. He made his .... after examining several models. (choose).

72. His .... of the duke was clear to all. (hate).
73. At one time, there was a great .... in the church. (revive).
74. Modern weapons of war cause great .... (destroy).

The MASCULINE gender of WOMAN is MAN. Name the MASCULINE gender of the word *in italics* in each sentence.
75. The *duchess* arrived with the ....
76. The *duck* and the .... walked across the road.
77. His *daughter* is married to my ....
78. The .... and the *maid-servant* were dismissed.
79. A .... and a *tabby-cat* sat on the mat.
80. The .... and *countess* attended the meeting.

Complete the following:—
81. As .... as a BEE.
82. As .... as a LAMB.
83. As .... as a HATTER.
84. As .... as a MULE.
85. As .... as an EEL.
86. As .... as a CHURCH MOUSE.

Write the SINGULAR of the following PLURAL nouns.
87. Gases   88. Cities
89. Leaves   90. Potatoes
91. Mice   92. Knives

Read the following and then answer the questions below:—

I Reach the Niger

It is impossible to describe the joy that arose in my mind when I looked around and concluded that I was out of danger. I felt like one recovered from a sickness; I breathed freer; I found unusual lightness in my limbs; even the desert looked pleasant, and I dreaded nothing so much as falling in with some wandering parties of Moors, who might even convey me back to the land of thieves and murderers from which I had just escaped.

I soon became sensible, however, that my position was deplorable, for I had no means of procuring food, nor prospect of finding water.

About ten o'clock, perceiving a herd of goats feeding close to the road, I took a circuitous route to avoid being seen, and continued travelling through the wilderness, directing my course, by compass nearly east-south-east, in order to reach as soon as possible some town or village of the kingdom of Bambarra.

'TRAVELS IN AFRICA'
—Mungo Park.

93. Why was I feeling happy? (I was out of danger; recovered from illness; breathing freely; the desert looked nice).

94. Why didn't I want to meet the Moors? (I was too tired; I didn't like them; I wasn't properly dressed; I didn't want to be taken back).

95. How was my position deplorable? (I was not safe; I had no food and water; I had come a long way; I was exhausted).

96. What did I avoid? (The kingdom of Bambarra; the wilderness; the herd of goats; the village).

97. How did I find my way? (Asked people; by compass; following the roads; watching the stars).

98. What looked pleasant? (The desert; the water; the sky; the animals).

70

99. What is a CIRCUITOUS route? (A round track; a short cut; a curious route; a roundabout route).
100. What word could have been used instead of DREADED? (Drawn; feared; wanted; refused).

EXERCISE 12

Write down a word which could be used instead of the word or words *in italics*. The first is done for you.

The boy quarrelled with *the boy's* friend. (his).

1. As the ship arrived at the port, the pilot met the *ship*.
2. Jane told *Jane's* mother that she was ill.
3. The boy was injured when the car hit *the boy*.
4. *Fred and Tom* are going fishing.
5. The boys' father told *the boys* that they could go.
6. Mary and Molly are popular with *Mary's and Molly's* friends.

Here are some punctuation marks:—(. , ? ! ").
Punctuate these sentences and remember to put in capital letters:—

7. do you need another pencil asked the teacher
8. you will never catch the bristol train said pat
9. mr smith is going to leeds on friday
10. come here demanded jack i want you
11. mrs jones said i am going to live in duke street
12. i havent seen harry since april

Read the sentence at (*a*) and then at (*b*):—

(*a*) David put *the* bird in the cage
(*b*) The bird *was put* in the cage by David.

Notice that the meaning is the same in (*a*) and (*b*).

71

Now write each of these sentences in the same way as
(b), starting with the word *in italics* in the *(a)* sentence.

13. *(a)* Marjory put *the* letter in the box.
    (b) ....
14. *(a)* Jack carried *the* coal into the shed.
    (b) ....
15. *(a)* Pamela tied *the* rope to the post.
    (b) ....
16. *(a)* Jean and Susan washed *the* dishes.
    (b) ....
17. *(a)* The referee started *the* game on time.
    (b) ....
18. *(a)* Fred's horse won *the* third race.
    (b) ....

The following words are nearly the same in meaning.
Write one in each sentence below:—
   Closed; stopped; ended; finished; concluded;
completed.
19. The clock .... at five o'clock.
20. I have .... all my sums.
21. The work on the building was .... in time.
22. The concert .... with the National Anthem.
23. After collecting £100, they .... the account.
24. Do you remember how the play .... ?

The following words end in ' ery ' or in ' ary.' Write
the words down.
25. A large blood vessel is called an art***.
26. In a factory there is a lot of machin***.
27. It is sometimes necess*** to be cautious.
28. Grain is stored in a gran***.
29. People, when they die, are buried in a cemet***.
30. The club has appointed a new secret***.

Place the following groups in alphabetical order:—
31. ask; come; divide; believe; fly
32. Some; sort; since; sew; sang
33. Piano; polo; punch; perch; pinch
34. Run; queen; match; mince; touch
35. Funny; fury; fume; fur; frost
36. Thimble; tumble; start; stop; thistle

One word in each group names the class to which the others belong. Spot this word.
37. Boys; girls; men; people; women.
38. Dinner; meals; tea; breakfast; supper.
39. Furniture; chair; sideboard; table; bookcase.
40. Turkey; goose; hen; poultry; duck.
41. Beans; parsnips; carrots; leeks; vegetables.
42. Wasp; fly; insect; ant; bee.

Read this poem and then answer the questions that follow.

Flower Chorus

Oh, such a commotion under the ground
When March called " Ho, there! ho! "
Such spreading of rootlets far and wide
Such whispering to and fro!
" Are you ready? " the Snowdrop asked,
" 'Tis time to start you know."
" Almost my dear " the Scilla replied
" I'll follow as soon as you go."
Then " Ha! ha! ha! " a chorus came
Of laughter sweet and low
Of millions of flowers under the ground,
Yes, millions, beginning to grow.
" I'll promise my blossoms " the Crocus said

" When I hear the blackbird sing,"
" And straight thereafter," Narcissus cried,
" My silver and gold I'll bring."
" And ere they are dulled," another spoke,
" The Hyacinth bells shall ring."
But the Violet only murmured " I'm here,"
And sweet grew the air of spring.
Then " Ha! ha! ha!" a chorus came
Of laughter sweet and low
Of millions of flowers under the ground,
Yes, millions, beginning to grow.

R. W. Emerson

43. What called " Ho there! ho! ", ? (The whispering roots; March; millions of flowers; the blackbird).
44. Which flower was first out of the ground? (Crocus; Narcissus; Snowdrop; Scilla).
45. What laughed " Ha ! ha ! ha! " ? (Millions of flowers; The Scilla; the Blackbird; the rootlets).
46. What was the Crocus waiting for? (The Snowdrop to bloom; the Violet; the blackbird to sing; the Hyacinth).
47. Which flower did the Narcissus follow? (The Violet; Hyacinth; Scilla; Crocus).
48. What does " *Ere* they are dulled " mean? (Now; before; after; noon).
49. Which word means the same as COMMOTION? (Song; noise; whisper; laughter).
50. What is the meaning of MURMURED? (Spoke low; whispered; shouted; motioned).

Give ONE word for the following:—
51. A child whose parents are dead.
52. A man about to be married.

53. A person who travels to this country to live here.
54. A person who eats too much.
55. A person travelling on foot.
56. A woman whose husband is dead.

A very small quantity of salt is called a GRAIN of salt. Write the name used for a very small quantity of the following:—

57. A .... of grass. 58. A .... of wood.
59. A .... of paper. 60. An .... of energy.
61. A .... of tea.   62. A .... of light.

Which is the correct word in the brackets?
63. You should not have gone (there; their).
64. (Were; where) did you buy your paints?
65. The guide cried, " (Hear; here) we are at last."
66. I called at (there; their) house yesterday.
67. I didn't know you (where; were) coming to town.
68. I saw him but I didn't (hear; here) him.

Write these addresses in full. Here is one done for you:
   High St. = High Street.
69. Smalldon Ave. = ...
70. New Rd. = ...
71. Martin Terr. = ...
72. Nott Sq. = ...
73. Bryn Cres. = ...
74. Doon Pl. = ...

Which is the correct word in each brackets?
75. The birds (flue; flew) through the window.
76. I passed the (nun; none) in the street.
77. The baby has (groan; grown) since I saw him.

78. We could hear the (cheep; cheap) of the sparrow.
79. The lion is a beast of (pray; prey).
80. The (rays; raise) of the sun were quite warm.

Give one word for:—
81. A young bear; ....
82. A young goat; ....
83. A young owl; ....
84. A young wasp; ....
85. A young eel; ....
86. A young bird; ....

Read this story and then answer the questions below.

Carried off by Pirates

One day Jack and I were enjoying ourselves in the water, preparatory to going on a fishing excursion; for Peterkin had kept us in such constant supply of hogs that we had become quite tired of pork, and desired a change.

Peterkin had stretched himself on a ledge of rock, while we were creeping among the rocks below. Happening to look up, I observed Peterkin cutting the most extraordinary capers and making violent gesticulations for us to come up; so I gave Jack a push and rose immediately.

"A sail! a sail!—Ralph look,—Jack, away on the horizon there, just over the entrance to the lagoon!" cried Peterkin, as we scrambled up the rocks.

"So it is, and a schooner too!" said Jack, as he proceeded hastily to dress.

'CORAL ISLAND'
R. M. Ballantyne.

87. What does "Preparatory to" mean: (Before; at the time; after; preparing).
88. Which word could be used instead of "Excursion"? (Exit; express; trip; exhibition).
89. What is constant supply? (Irregular; canned; copious; regular).
90. Why did Ralph and Jack go fishing? (They needed food; they enjoyed fishing; they needed a change of food; to pass the time).
91. Which word is OPPOSITE to "Violent"? (Vicious; gentle; dangerous; ferocious).
92. Why did Peterkin call the others? (He saw a sail; he was injured; he was afraid; he could not move).
93. Which word is OPPOSITE to "Entrance"? (Opening; beginning; exit; excuse).
94. What word means nearly the same as "Proceeded"? (Performed; persuaded; started; stopped).

Here are two sentences (*a*) and (*b*), each containing the same word used with a different meaning:—

(*a*) Peggy is not so *well* today.

(*b*) The water was carried from the *well*.

Now write three pairs of sentences using each word in capitals so that it has two different meanings in (*a*) and (*b*).

95. KIND. (*a*) ....
96.   (*b*) ....
97. POST. (*a*) ....
98.   (*b*) ....
99. LIES. (*a*) ....
100.   (*b*) ....

EXERCISE 13

Think of a suitable word to complete each sentence:—
1. He is an authority .... gardening.
2. The stranger hid .... the door.
3. My brother differs .... me in many ways.
4. The young lady takes a great pride .... her appearance.
5. I pushed the letter .... the front door.
6. We were greatly impressed .... his speech.

———

This paragraph is not complete, for there are eight phrases missing. Here they are, but not in the right order:—

ten o'clock / made myself useful / near the lake / just before / pack the food / only three / playing with / short distance.

Place each phrase in its proper place:—
7. Father was busy helping mother to ....
8. for the picnic while I .... too.
9. Irene, who was the youngest and ....
10. years old, could not help; she sat ....
11. her doll. We set off at .... and arrived
12. .... noon.
13. We walked a .... and finally selected
14. a quiet spot under the trees ....

———

Which is the correct word in each bracket?
15. Of the three pigs, the first was the (fatter; fattest).
16. Jean is the (youngest; younger) of the two girls.
17. The four boys were fast, but Peter was the (faster; fastest).
18. Both buildings are ugly, but the tall one is the (uglier; ugliest).

19. Harry was the (biggest; bigger) boy of all.
20. Of the five puppies, the brown one is the (weaker; weakest).

Write the correct form of the word in capitals.
21. Percy had (   ) the cake before we arrived. EAT.
22. All outside taps (   ) last night. FREEZE.
23. Susan was (   ) by the terrier. BITE.
24. The lady driver (   ) to slow down. BEGIN.
25. Tom was being (   ) mad with pain. DRIVE.
26. Tea is (   ) in Kenya. GROW.

Write the word in each group which is the name of the class to which the other four belong:
27. Jacket; trousers; garment; blouse; waistcoat.
28. Glasgow; London; Cardiff; City; Manchester.
29. Sandal; footwear; boot; slipper; shoe.
30. Hear; sense; see; feel; taste.
31. Mississippi; Amazon; River; Nile; Niger.
32 Flower; pansy; tulip; crocus; rose.

Complete each sentence by adding one of these words:—
    What; who; whom; whose; which; that.
33. We spoke to the man .... had crossed the Atlantic.
34. I liked the person to .... I hired the boat.
35. She asked me, " .... of these do you prefer? "
36. The nurse attended the woman .... nose was broken.
37. Nobody seemed to hear .... he said.
38. This is the lawn .... my father was cutting.

79

Name the correct word in each bracket:—

39. I have (forgot; forgotten) to write home.
40. Sam (had; got) a nasty accident last week.
41. Between you and (I; me), he is very foolish.
42. This dress is nearly (worn; wore) out.
43. I have never seen (any; none) of them.
44. To (who; whom) does the house belong?

———————

In column A is the first part of a sentence. The second part is in Column B, but NOT in its proper place. Read the six mixed sentences and write them down in correct order.

A	B
45. The little puppy	can say a few words
46. A typewriter	came ashore on leave
47. The fishmonger	sells cotton
48. The draper	played with a bone
49. The sailor	is very useful
50. My parrot	sells plaice

———————

Read this description and then answer the questions that follow.

William of Orange

He had a thin and weak body, and was of a clear and delicate constitution. His behaviour was solemn and serious, seldom cheerful, and but with a few, he spoke little and very slowly.

He was an exact observer of men and things. His strength lay rather in sound judgment than in imagination. His genius lay chiefly in war, in which his courage was more admired than his conduct.

80

On the battlefield great errors were often committed by him, but his courage set things right, as it inflamed those who were about him.

Gilbert Burnet (1643-1715).

If the following statements are true, write ' T ', but if untrue, write ' U'.

51. William had a strong constitution.
52. He was a man of sound judgment.
53. His courage annoyed others.
54. He spoke a great deal.
55. He was a quick speaker.
56. He made mistakes on the battlefield.
57. He was very fond of joking.
58. He was extremely clever in war.

Some words are used to add meaning to a VERB, ADJECTIVE or another ADVERB. Here are some examples:

(a) The nursemaid *gently* rocked the baby to sleep.
The ' rocking ' is described by the word ' gently'.
(b) The train arrived *late*.
' Late ' tells us ' when ' the train arrived.

Adverbs that answer the question How? When, or Where? are used with verbs.

Now add a suitable adverb to these verbs *in italics* by asking How? when? or where?

59. The man *collapsed* .... on the pavement.
60. The next train will *arrive* ....
61. The girl *sang* .... at the concert.
62. Both the boys *did* .... in the examination.
63. Everybody *laughed* .... at the joke.
64. The spectators *cheered* .... as he scored.

Complete the following:—
65. My friend said that he felt as .... as a fiddle.
66. In spite of the rain, I arrived as .... as a bone.
67. The new boy is as .... as mustard.
68. This parcel is as .... as a feather.
69. In a few moments I felt as .... as rain.
70. The old man is as .... as a doorpost.

Name the word in each bracket which must be used to make the sentence correct:—
71. (Who; whom) did you see at the bazaar?
72. He is not as old as (I; me).
73. The (better; best) team won the cup match.
74. Frank has (broke; broken) his arm.
75. The scout admitted he (did; done) it.
76. We returned home as (quickly; quick) as we could.

We often use words in pairs. Here is an example:—
   The car went by FITS and STARTS.
Spot the missing word in each of these sentences:—
77. There are WAYS and .... of making him obey.
78. His whole HEART and .... is in the work.
79. I bought the ONE and .... set left in the sale.
80. There was a big HUE and .... after the thief.
81. Don't tell him yet, he'll only RANT and ....
82. The game was a real ROUGH and ....

Sentences are first divided into two parts, the NAMING part containing the subject (noun and pronoun) and the TELLING or DOING part containing the VERB. This part is called the PREDICATE and the naming part is known as the SUBJECT.

Examples:—

Subject	*predicate*
The little boy	fell off the ladder.
I	like plum pudding.

Divide these in the same way:—

	Subject	Predicate
83. A carpenter uses a chisel.	....	....
84. The driver crashed into the wall.	....	....
85. Our school party was very enjoyable.	....	....
86. Marconi was a famous inventor.	....	....
87. My parents visited the school.	....	....
88. We decided to buy a new set.	....	....

The words ' is not ' can be written in a contracted form as ' isn't '. There is ONE of these contracted words in each sentence. Write it in full.

89. The men *aren't* ready to start the work.
90. Hugh *doesn't* know whether he can go.
91. *We're* hoping it will be fine tomorrow.
92. I wrote to May to ask if *she'll* join us.
93. Jack shouted, " *It's* too late now".
94. If *you're* early, you can help me.

Write the opposite to each of these words by using the PREFIXES shown:—

In; im; dis; ir; un; mis.

95. Advantage................... 96. fire ....
97. moral .... 98. visible ....
99. screw .... 100. reverent ....

EXERCISE 14

Read the first sentence and then write a suitable word to complete the second sentence, without changing the meaning:—

1. This box belongs to me.   This box is ....
2. This book belongs to you.   This book is ....
3. The football belongs to them.   The football is ....
4. The cap belongs to him.   The cap is ....
5. The plot belongs to us.   The plot is ....
6. The beads belong to her.   The beads are ....

Write ONE word which can be used to take the place of the words *in italics*:—

7. The girl shouted *with excitement*.
8. The man hit me *without intending to do so*.
9. The boy dived *without fear*, into the deep water.
10. The doctor dressed the wound *without causing pain*.
11. He crept from the room *without making a noise*.
12. The waitress left *in a hurry*.

Complete the following:—

13. POLICEMAN is to THIEF as GAMEKEEPER is to ....
14. PEEL is to APPLE as .... is to EGG.

15. DOZEN is to GROSS as ONE is to ....
16. JANUARY is to FEBRUARY as JULY is to ....
17. BIRD is to WING as .... is to FIN.
18. BULLET is to RIFLE as ARROW is to ....

Write down the TWO words in each group, which are associated with or are part of the word in capitals.
19. TREE. Leaf; pole; kale; bark; strip.
20. MOUTH. Pull; push; taste; chew; nose.
21. HORSE. Coach; bridle; train; car; mane.
22. CLOCK. Face; handle; hands; cue; tell.
23. BATH. Tiles; plug; bare; tapestry; clothes.
24. SAUCEPAN. Spring; lid; sauce; handle; pan.

The mark (') known as the APOSTROPHE is used to show ownership or possession.

The horse's tail . . . this is the tail of ONE horse.

The horses' tails . . . these are the tails of MORE THAN ONE horse.

Write out the following with the apostrophes in their proper position.
25. The authors book was sold by auction.
26. The mens clothes were destroyed in the fire.
27. The ladys umbrella is lost.
28. I called at my daughters school.
29. The babies bonnets are made of wool.
30. I was tired after the days work.

Name the VERB in each of these proverbs:—
31. A still tongue makes a wise head.
32. Too many cooks spoil the broth.
33. Every cloud has a silver lining.

34. A stitch in time saves nine.
35. Empty vessels make most sound.
36. Faint heart never won fair lady.

———————

Look at the two words in Col. A and then in Col. B. The two words in each column are related in the same way. Under each pair in Col. A add a word so as to make a similar pair. One is done for you.

In—out; top—bottom; few—many. (Pairs are OPPOSITE).

Col. A	Col. B
37. Lady—ladies	Church—churches
Child—	
38. Some—sum	Pain—pane
Real—	
39. Sing—sang	Swim—swam
Sink—	
40. Bee—hive	Bird—nest
Pig—	
41. Nephew—niece	Man—woman
Uncle—	
42. Fast—quick	Small—little
Broad—	

———————

Use ONE word instead of the words *in italics*, without changing the meaning of the sentence.

43. The teacher said that *the teacher* was very pleased.
44. Joan's mother gave *Joan* a new hat.
45. Miss Smith asked the boys if *the boys* would help her.
46. The pupils asked *the pupils'* teacher if they could play.

86